Reading and Writing

Helpful hints for parents

- Start at the beginning of the book and try to work through the activities in order.
- Encourage your child to work independently as much as possible, without referring to the answers!
- Discuss any areas that your child finds particularly tricky and don't worry if he or she finds any of the exercises too difficult. Remember, children learn different things at different rates.
- Give help and lots of praise, rewarding your child by adding stickers to the reward certificate for great work and effort.
- Once you have completed the workbook, move on to the practice pages bound in the centre.

Autumn Publishing

www.autumnchildrensbooks.co.uk

Missing vowels

Add the missing vowels, **a**, **e**, **i**, **o** and **u**, to this passage.

Every tre_ in a r_inforest is fo_d, shelter and hom_ to lots of an_mals. Moles and r_dents dig am_ng the ro_ts. Woodpeck_rs p_ck at the b_rk for _nsects. Sn_kes slith_r through the br_nches and le_pards drag the_r food to th_ fork of a tree tr_nk.

Larg_ creatures such as b_rds, rept_les and mamm_ls will come _nd go, b_t some _nimals may live their wh_le lives in on_ tree.

More missing vowels

Add the missing vowels to this poem.

The Owl and the Pussy Cat

The Owl __nd the P__ssy Cat went to s__a

In a be__utiful pea gr__en boat;

They t__ok some h__ney, and plenty of m__ney

Wr__pped up in a f__ve pound n__te.

The Owl lo__ked up to the st__rs abov__,

And sang to a sm__ll guitar,

"O lov__ly Pussy, O Pussy my lov__,

Wh__t a beautif__l Pussy you are, you __re!

What __ beautiful Pussy y__u are!"

Pussy sa__d to the __wl, "You elegant fowl!

How charmingly swe__t you sing!

O l__t us be married; too long we h__ve tarried:

But wh__t shall we do for a ring?"

Th__y sailed aw__y, for a year and a d__y,

To the land wher__ the Bong-tree grows;

And there in a wood a Piggy-wig sto__d,

With a r__ng at the end of his nose, his n__se,

With a ring at the __nd of his nos__.

Edward Lear

In a muddle

These instructions for making bread rolls have got muddled.
Put them in the correct order by numbering the boxes.

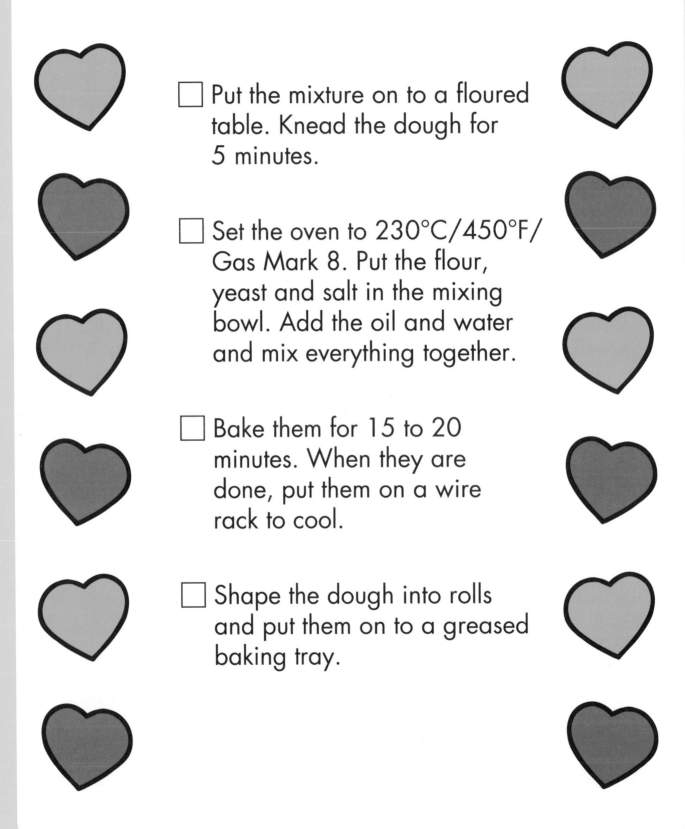

☐ Put the mixture on to a floured table. Knead the dough for 5 minutes.

☐ Set the oven to 230°C/450°F/ Gas Mark 8. Put the flour, yeast and salt in the mixing bowl. Add the oil and water and mix everything together.

☐ Bake them for 15 to 20 minutes. When they are done, put them on a wire rack to cool.

☐ Shape the dough into rolls and put them on to a greased baking tray.

More in a muddle

This story has been muddled up.
Put the story in order by numbering the boxes.

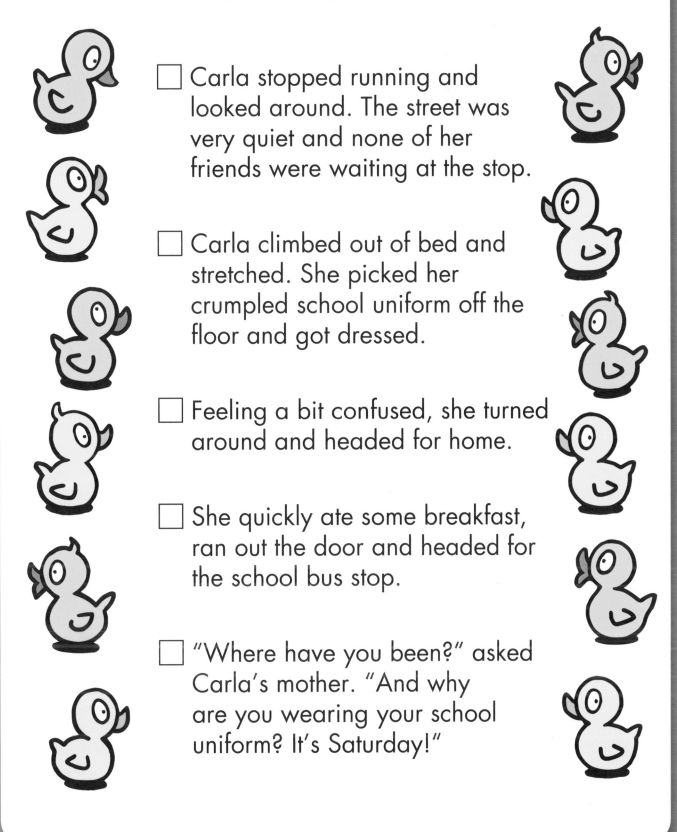

☐ Carla stopped running and looked around. The street was very quiet and none of her friends were waiting at the stop.

☐ Carla climbed out of bed and stretched. She picked her crumpled school uniform off the floor and got dressed.

☐ Feeling a bit confused, she turned around and headed for home.

☐ She quickly ate some breakfast, ran out the door and headed for the school bus stop.

☐ "Where have you been?" asked Carla's mother. "And why are you wearing your school uniform? It's Saturday!"

Jumbled beginnings

The beginnings of these three traditional tales have been jumbled up.
Can you rewrite them in the correct order?

in a far away land, there lived an Long ago, Emperor who was very vain.

_____

_____

_____

called Hansel and Gretel. A long time ago, who had two lovely children there lived a kind woodcutter

_____

_____

_____

the henhouse to collect the eggs One day, a farmer went into and was astonished to find a golden egg.

_____

_____

_____

Word search

Look in the word search grid for 10 number words.
You will find them by reading across or down.
Draw a ring around the words as you find them.

N	E	R	T	N	H	I	M	O
I	W	S	C	S	E	V	E	N
N	P	R	N	E	O	R	P	E
E	T	J	I	U	E	X	Z	H
T	W	E	N	T	Y	R	J	U
E	R	I	D	H	F	B	Z	N
E	X	G	N	I	X	H	J	D
N	S	H	X	R	V	T	S	R
R	K	T	Y	T	X	N	D	E
T	N	E	U	E	K	I	O	D
G	O	E	I	E	U	H	E	N
T	E	N	X	N	Y	U	L	B
R	E	U	I	K	F	J	E	M
F	I	F	T	Y	N	O	V	R
O	S	E	B	V	X	P	E	O
F	O	U	R	T	E	E	N	P

Spellings

Put a tick next to the words that are spelled correctly and a cross next to those that are wrong. Correct the incorrect spellings and write them in the space at the bottom of the page.

☐ arrived

☐ trroubble

☐ reech

☐ money

☐ girafe

☐ beecause

☐ wheal

☐ question

☐ rubber

☐ clouwd

☐ clothes

☐ weight

More spellings

Put a tick next to the words that are spelled correctly and a cross next to those that are wrong. Correct the incorrect spellings and write them in the space at the bottom of the page.

☐ puddle   ☐ cuboard

☐ kitte   ☐ chicken

☐ packit   ☐ drawer

☐ trumpet   ☐ finished

☐ dificult   ☐ bottum

☐ person   ☐ appeer

Missing punctuation

This passage is missing its punctuation and capital letters.
Rewrite the passage, adding what is missing.

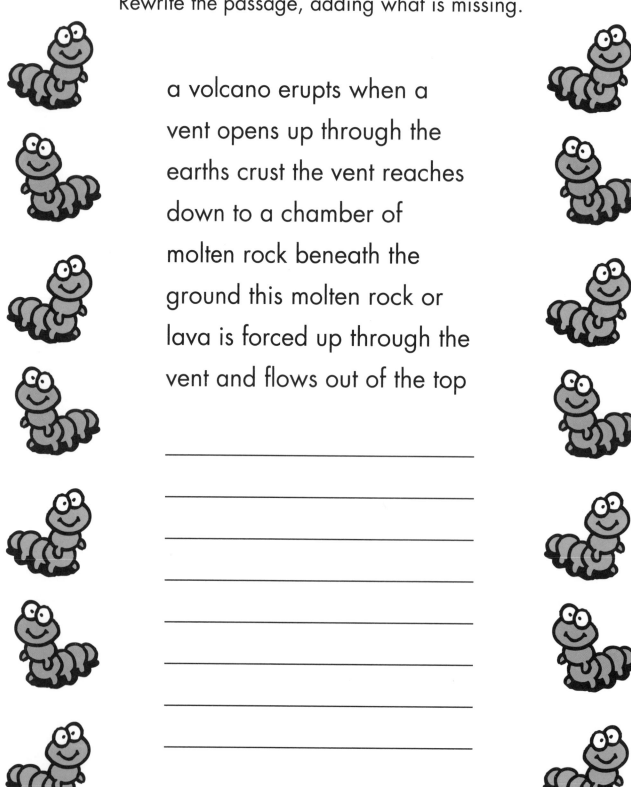

a volcano erupts when a
vent opens up through the
earths crust the vent reaches
down to a chamber of
molten rock beneath the
ground this molten rock or
lava is forced up through the
vent and flows out of the top

_____

_____

_____

_____

_____

_____

_____

More missing punctuation

These sentences are missing their punctuation and capital letters.
Rewrite the sentences, adding what is missing.

the curtains were drawn and the room was dark

who wants something to eat asked the teacher

the bucket was full of shells crabs pebbles and driftwood

stop shouted the traffic warden at the old lady

_____

_____

_____

_____

_____

_____

_____

_____

All in order

Write these words in alphabetical order.

clock _____

please _____

shrink _____

clothes _____

snake _____

flowers _____

pear _____

straight _____

washing _____

third _____

finished _____

different _____

Crossword

Use the clues to help you complete this crossword grid.
Follow the numbers across and down, and write the words in the grid.

Across
1. A book full of words and definitions.
2. A punctuation mark indicating a pause.
3. Past, present and future are all these.
4. These end with a question mark.

Down
2. The main divisions in a book.
5. There are 26 letters in ours.

Poetry corner

Add the missing letters to the nouns in this verse.
(Here's a clue: the poem rhymes!)

From a Railway Carriage

Faster than fairies, faster than
wit__es,

Bridges and houses, hedges
and ditches;

And charging along like troops
in a battle

All through the meadows the
horses and ca__le:

All of the sights of the hill
and the plain

Fly as thick as driving r___;

And ever again, in the wink of
an e__,

Painted stations whistle by.

Robert Louis Stevenson

READING AND WRITING PRACTICE
TRICKY WORDS

Underline the correct spelling each time. How did you score?

A

1. friend — freind
2. accidently — accidentally
3. greatful — grateful
4. heighth — height
5. library — librery
6. occasionally — occasionaly
7. untill — until
8. weather — wheather
9. wierd — weird
10. personal — personnal
11. mischievous — mischievious
12. calender — calendar
13. changeable — changible
14. rhythm — rythm
15. awkwerd — awkward

/15

B

1. believe — beleive
2. embarass — embarrass
3. foriegn — foreign
4. happend — happened
5. bought — borght
6. once — wonce
7. thort — thought
8. surround — suround
9. beautiful — beatiful
10. surprise — surprize
11. heard — heared
12. first — frist
13. agian — again
14. pritty — pretty
15. autunm — autumn

/15

SOUNDS THE SAME

Next to each word, write another word that sounds the same but is spelled differently.

1. sale _____

2. chute _____

3. paws _____

4. waste _____

5. billed _____

6. bored _____

7. flower _____

8. scene _____

9. way _____

10. grown _____

Choose three of your new words from the box above and write a full sentence for each one.

1. _____

_____

2. _____

_____

3. _____

_____

PUNCTUATION

Add the missing punctuation marks to these sentences.

1. The boy ran across the park, trying to catch his naughty dog

2. I'm definitely not going shopping in this weather, said Tamsin's mum

3. Help cried Jack I can't get out

4. What name is given to the person in charge of a boat or ship

5. Will you read me a bedtime story   Dean asked

6. The queue of people at the desk seemed to go on forever

7. Which season follows spring

8. Do you like bananas Would you rather have an apple asked David

9. The red door opened on to a beautiful garden, filled with flowers, trees and ornaments

10. Happy birthday   shouted Terry, as he jumped up from behind the sofa

TENSES

Write the past tense of each of these verbs.

A

1. walk _____
2. bend _____
3. shoot _____
4. buy _____
5. build _____
6. add _____
7. buy _____
8. catch _____
9. feed _____
10. bring _____
11. jump _____
12. sell _____
13. feed _____
14. speak _____
15. doodle _____

B

1. think _____
2. sit _____
3. hang _____
4. fight _____
5. lend _____
6. find _____
7. lose _____
8. lick _____
9. pay _____
10. send _____
11. spend _____
12. race _____
13. weep _____
14. paint _____
15. wrote _____

Handwriting practice

Practise your handwriting by copying the verse from the poem on the previous page. Remember to take care with the size of your letters and the spaces between words. Try to join your handwriting as much as you can.

From a Railway Carriage

_____

_____

_____

_____

_____

_____

_____

_____

Comprehension passage

Read this passage and answer the questions on the next page.

Whales of the South Pole

No ocean has as many whales as the Southern Ocean around the South Pole. There are two main whale groups. The toothed whales are hunters that can dive to great depths in search of prey. The baleen whales have large, flat plates of whalebone hanging from the upper jaw. They fill their mouths with sea water and then squeeze the water out through the baleen plates and swallow the trapped food. This food is made up of tiny organisms called 'plankton'.

Generally, these whales swim away from the Pole as winter approaches. They migrate towards warmer tropical waters and will stay there while the female whales give birth. Then in the spring, they head towards the Pole again, to feed on the plentiful food during the summer months.

Comprehension questions

Try to write your answers as complete sentences.

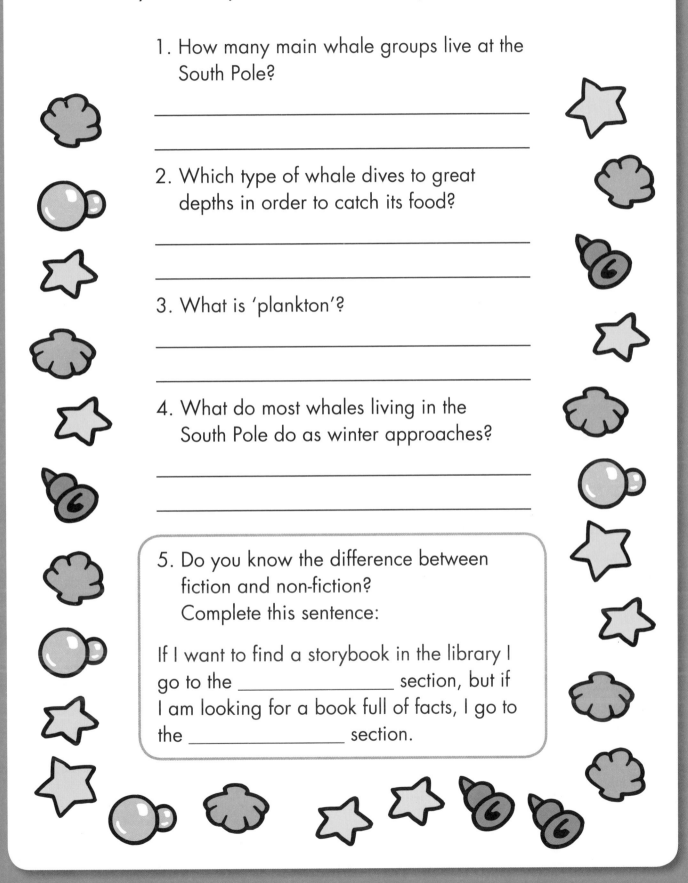

1. How many main whale groups live at the South Pole?

_____

_____

2. Which type of whale dives to great depths in order to catch its food?

_____

_____

3. What is 'plankton'?

_____

_____

4. What do most whales living in the South Pole do as winter approaches?

_____

_____

5. Do you know the difference between fiction and non-fiction?
Complete this sentence:

If I want to find a storybook in the library I go to the _____ section, but if I am looking for a book full of facts, I go to the _____ section.

Design a poster

Imagine your school is having a Christmas disco.
Use the information in the box to help you design
a poster that will encourage lots of people to come!

7.00pm, School Hall,
Saturday 12th December,
fancy dress, drinks and snacks,
music and dancing, festive fun

Wish you were here

Imagine you and your family are on holiday by the beach. Write a letter to your best friend and include the following information: where you are, what you have done, what you are going to do, and any other information you can think of.

Dear _____

_____

_____

_____

_____

_____

_____

_____

_____

_____

Tense time

Join each verb with its past tense.

move	arrived
bring	taught
speak	looked
take	wrote
teach	moved
come	saw
hold	took
arrive	held
write	brought
see	came
look	begged
beg	spoke

More tenses

Rewrite these sentences in the past tense.

Clive walks to the shops.

_____

The rabbit escapes from its hutch.

_____

She opens the book at the first page.

_____

He takes a sip from the tall glass.

_____

Leah plays her favourite song.

_____

The bear crawls back into its cave.

_____

Time to rhyme

Join the pairs of words that rhyme.

blue	sky
coal	flush
clean	so
main	flew
pie	bee
thin	luck
horse	pole
brush	been
stuck	pin
flea	heat
low	course
wheat	train

Writing a letter

Imagine you could write a letter to Snow White to warn her about her stepmother, the wicked queen. What good advice would you give her?

Dear Snow White,

_____

_____

_____

_____

_____

_____

_____

More letter writing

Imagine you could write a letter to the three little pigs from the fairy story.
What advice would you give them about the big bad wolf?

Dear Little Pigs,

_____

_____

_____

_____

_____

_____

_____

_____

_____

Sounds the same

Some words sound the same but mean different things.
Underline the correct word in each sentence.

Molly has to/two goldfish.

Jez had his hair/hare cut.

Lucy loves fairy tales/tails.

Jack stood bye/by
the gate.

Max has a book about
bears/bares.

Jo saw a deer/dear
in the wood.

There/their was a knock at
the door.

More sounds the same

Draw a line under the correct word in each sentence.

I hope it doesn't rain/rein.

Turn right/write at the junction.

We walked on the beech/beach.

They had there/their lunch.

Where/wear is the exit?

Let's have tee/tea.

What would/wood you like?

The dog found it's/its bone.

Answers

Missing vowels

tree	branches
rainforest	leopards
food	their
home	the
animals	trunk
rodents	Large
among	birds
roots	reptiles
Woodpeckers	mammals
peck	and
bark	but
insects	animals
Snakes	whole
slither	one

More missing vowels

and Pussy sea	sweet
beautiful green	let have
took honey money	what
Wrapped five note	They away day
looked stars above	where
small	stood
lovely love	ring nose
What beautiful are	end nose
a you	
said Owl	

In a muddle

2 Put the mixture on to a floured table. Knead the dough for 5 minutes.

1 Set the oven to 230°C/450°F/ Gas Mark 8. Put the flour, yeast and salt in the mixing bowl. Add the oil and water and mix everything together.

4 Bake them for 15 to 20 minutes. When they are done, put them on a wire rack to cool.

3 Shape the dough into rolls and put them on to a greased baking tray.

More in a muddle

3 Carla stopped running and looked around. The street was very quiet and none of her friends were waiting at the stop.

1 Carla climbed out of bed and stretched. She picked her crumpled school uniform off the floor and got dressed.

4 Feeling a bit confused, she turned around and headed for home.

2 She quickly ate some breakfast, ran out the door and headed for the school bus stop.

5 "Where have you been?" asked Carla's mother. "And why are you wearing your school uniform? It's Saturday!"

Jumbled beginnings

Long ago, in a far away land, there lived an Emperor who was very vain.

A long time ago, there lived a kind woodcutter who had two lovely children called Hansel and Gretel.

One day, a farmer went into the henhouse to collect the eggs and was astonished to find a golden egg.

Word search

```
N E R T N H I M O O
I W S C S E V E N N
N P R N E O R P E E
E T J I U E X Z J H
T W E N T Y R J U U
E R I D H F B Z N N
E X G N I X H J D D
N S H X R V T S R R
R K T Y T X N D T E
T N E U E K I O O D
G O E I E U H E N
T E N I E Y U L E
R E U I K F J E M
F I F T Y N O V E R
O S E B V X P E O O
F O U R T E E N P
```

Spellings

✔arrived	✘troubble
✘reech	✔money
✘girafe	✘beecause
✘wheal	✔question
✔rubber	✘clouwd
✔clothes	✔weight

reach	trouble
giraffe	because
wheel	cloud

More spellings

✔puddle	✘cuboard
✘kitte	✔chicken
✘packit	✔drawer
✔trumpet	✔finished
✘dificult	✘bottum
✔person	✘appeer

kite	cupboard
packet	bottom
difficult	appear

Answers

Missing punctuation

A volcano erupts when a vent opens up through the Earth's crust. The vent reaches down to a chamber of molten rock beneath the ground. This molten rock, or lava, is forced up through the vent and flows out of the top.

More missing punctuation

The curtains were drawn and the room was dark.

"Who wants something to eat?" asked the teacher.

The bucket was full of shells, crabs, pebbles and driftwood.

"Stop!" shouted the traffic warden at the old lady.

All in order

clock
clothes
different
finished
flowers
pear
please
shrink
snake
straight
third
washing

Crossword

Across:
1. DICTIONARY
2. COMMA
3. TENSES
4. QUESTIONS

Down:
1. CHAPTERS
5. ALPHABET (ALPHA BET)

Poetry corner

Faster than fairies, faster than wit**ch**es,
Bridges and houses, hedges and ditches;
And charging along like troops in a battle
All through the meadows the horses and ca**tt**le:
All of the sights of the hill and the plain
Fly as thick as driving r**ain**;
And ever again, in the wink of an e**ye**,
Painted stations whistle by.

Comprehension passage

1. Two main whale groups live at the South Pole.
2. The toothed whales dive to great depths in search of prey.
3. Plankton is made up of tiny organisms and is food for the whales.
4. They migrate towards warmer tropical waters and stay there while the females give birth.
5. If I want to find a storybook in the library I go to the **fiction** section, but if I am looking for a book full of facts, I go to the **non-fiction** section.

Tense time

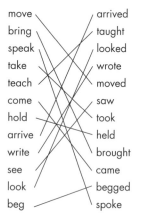

move — moved
bring — brought
speak — spoke
take — took
teach — taught
come — came
hold — held
arrive — arrived
write — wrote
see — saw
look — looked
beg — begged

More tenses

Clive walked to the shops.

The rabbit escaped from its hutch.

She opened the book at the first page.

He took a sip from the tall glass.

Leah played her favourite song.

The bear crawled back into its cave.

Time to rhyme

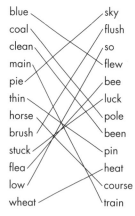

blue — flew
coal — pole
clean — been
main — train
pie — sky
thin — pin
horse — course
brush — flush
stuck — luck
flea — bee
low — so
wheat — heat

Sounds the same

Molly has to/**two** goldfish.

Jez had his **hair**/hare cut.

Lucy loves fairy **tales**/tails.

Jack stood bye/**by** the gate.

Max has a book about **bears**/bares.

Jo saw a **deer**/dear in the wood.

There/their was a knock at the door.

More sounds the same

I hope it doesn't **rain**/rein.

Turn **right**/write at the junction.

We walked on the beech/**beach**.

They had there/**their** lunch.

Where/wear is the exit?

Let's have tee/**tea**.

What **would**/wood you like?

The dog found it's/**its** bone.